Peter Ilyich
TCHAIKOVSKY

SLEEPING BEAUTY
Suite from the Ballet
Op. 66a
(Simpson)

Study Score
Partitur

SERENISSIMA MUSIC, INC.

CONTENTS

1. Introduction et La Fée des Lilas 1

2. Pas d'action 28

3. Pas de caractère 50

4. Panorama 54

5. Valse 73

ORCHESTRA

Piccolo, 2 Flutes, 2 Oboes, English Horn, 2 Clarinets, 2 Bassoons

4 Horns, 2 Cornets, 2 Trumpets, 3 Trombones, Tuba

Timpani, Triangle, Side Drum, Bass Drum, Cymbals, Glockenspiel

Harp

Violins I, Violins II, Violas, Violoncellos, Basses

Duration: ca. 20 minutes

Edwin F. Kalmus, LC
P. O. Box 5011
Boca Raton, FL 33431-0811
Phone: 561-241-6340; 800-434-6340
Fax: 561-241-6347
Website: www.kalmus-music.com

SLEEPING BEAUTY SUITE

Op. 66a

1. Introduction et La Fée des Lilas

*Original: Cornets, Trumpets in A

SERENISSIMA MUSIC, INC.

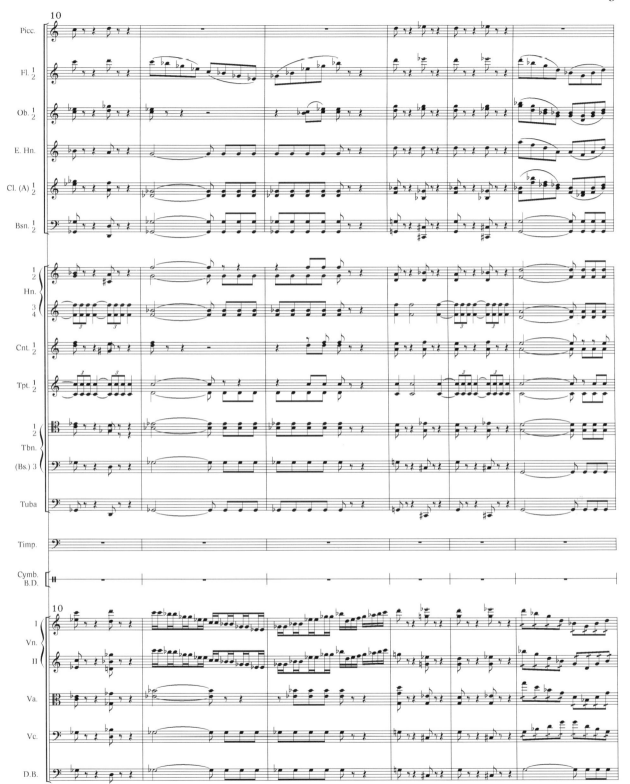

4

1.1. Hn. 3, m. 20/3: JRFS, MFS have ♪ ⁊ ⁊ ♪

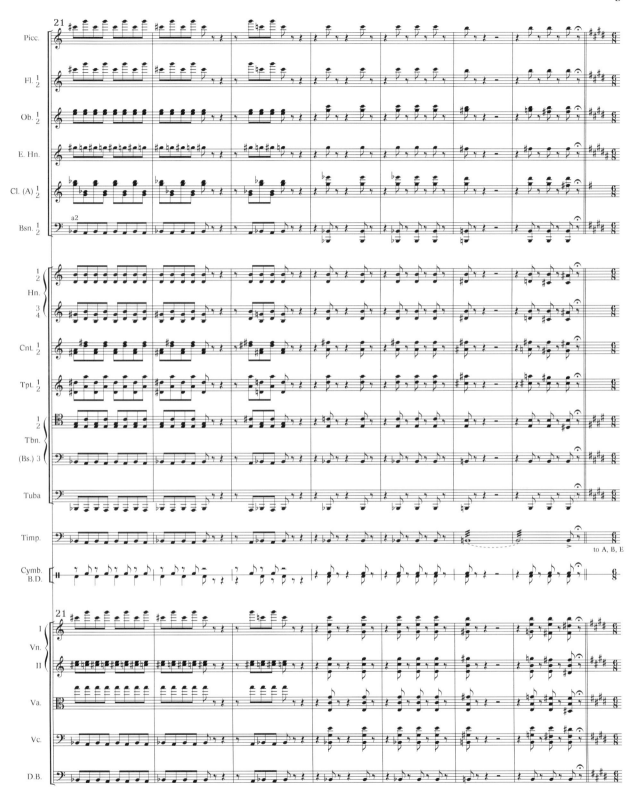

La Fée des Lilas

1.2. Bn. 2, m. 35: JRFS has G♯

8

1.3. Hp., m. 40–41: JRFS has the music in 42–43 here also.

10

40437

14

1.4. Cl. 2, m. 62: JRFS has G♭

16

40437

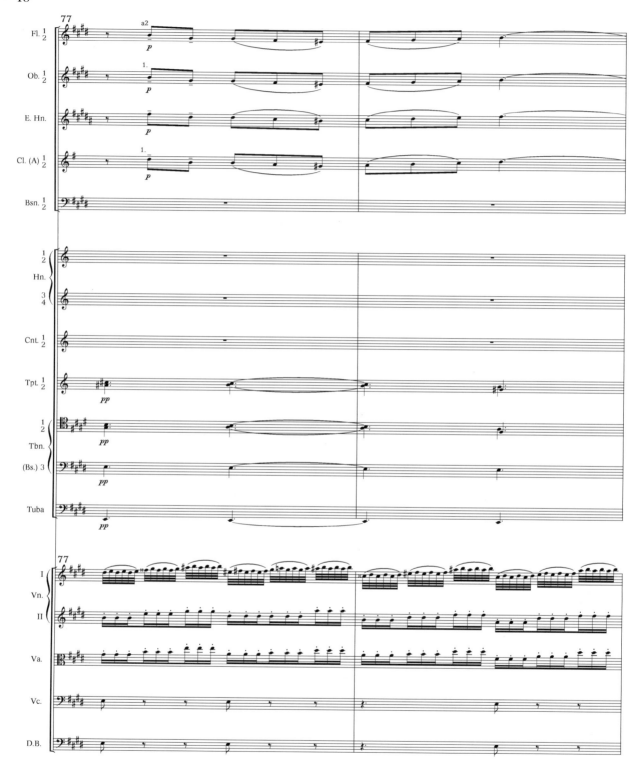

1.5. Cnts., mm. 81–88: JRFS assigns this to Tpts.

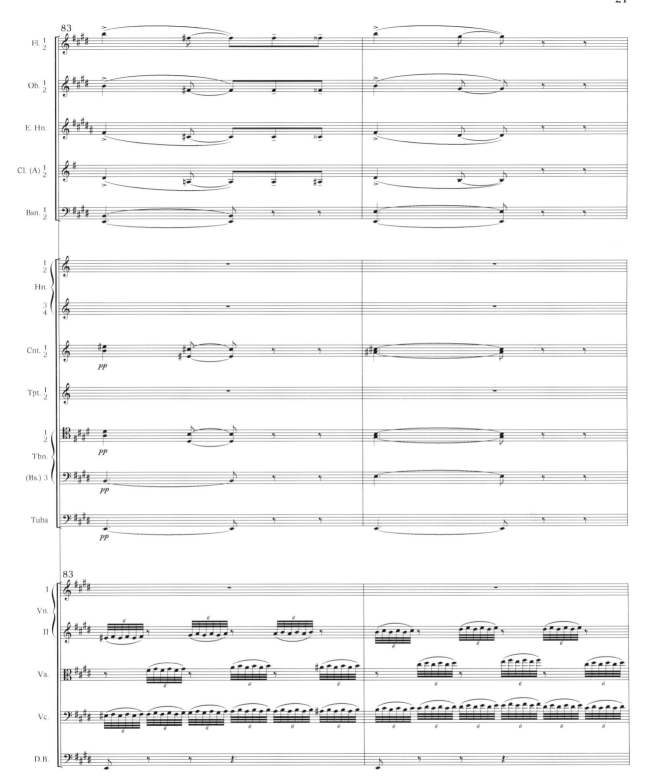

21

40437

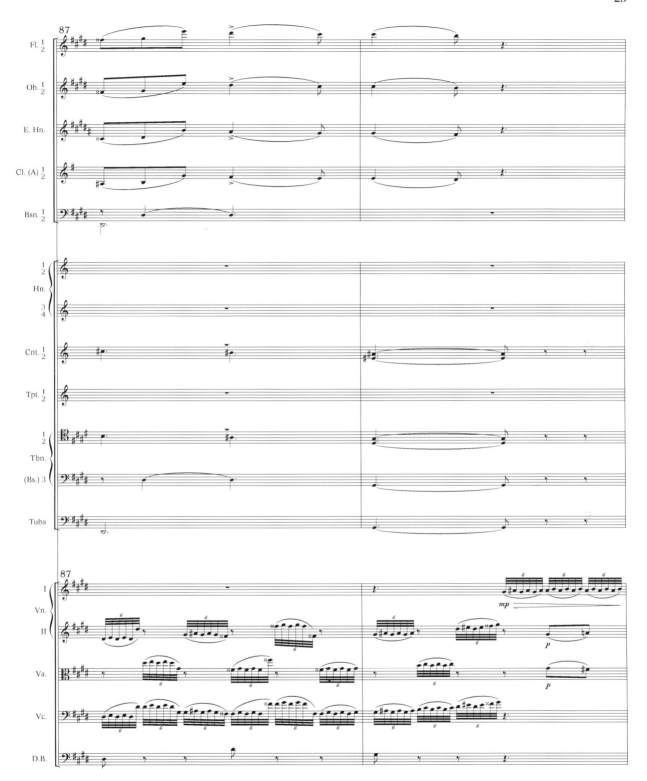

2. Pas d'Action

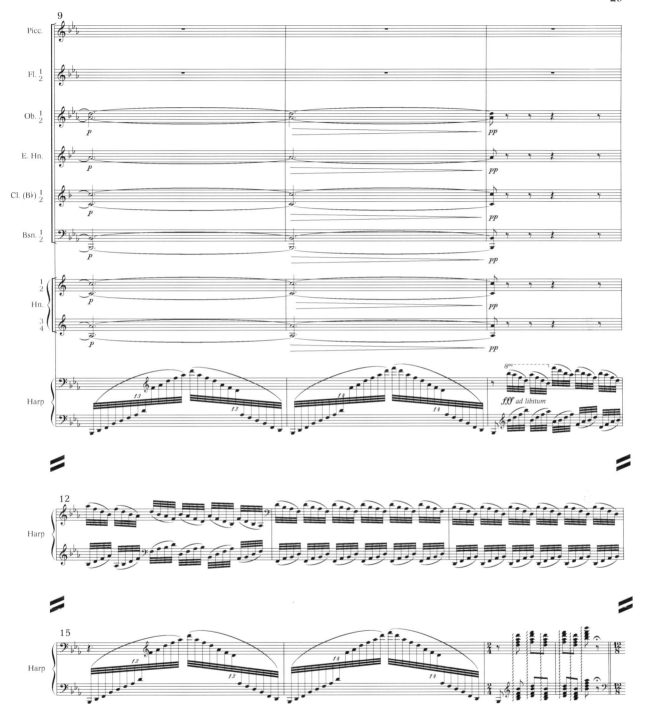

30

40437

32

40437

34

2.1. Fls., Cls., m. 32: JRFS has *fff*

40437

38

40437

40

40437

44

40437

Molto sostenuto, quasi più andante

48

3. Pas de Caractère

52

40437

4. Panorama

56

40437

58

40437

64

40437

68

40437

72

5. Valse

74

40437

5.1. Bns., m. 35: MFS has

78

40437

82

40437

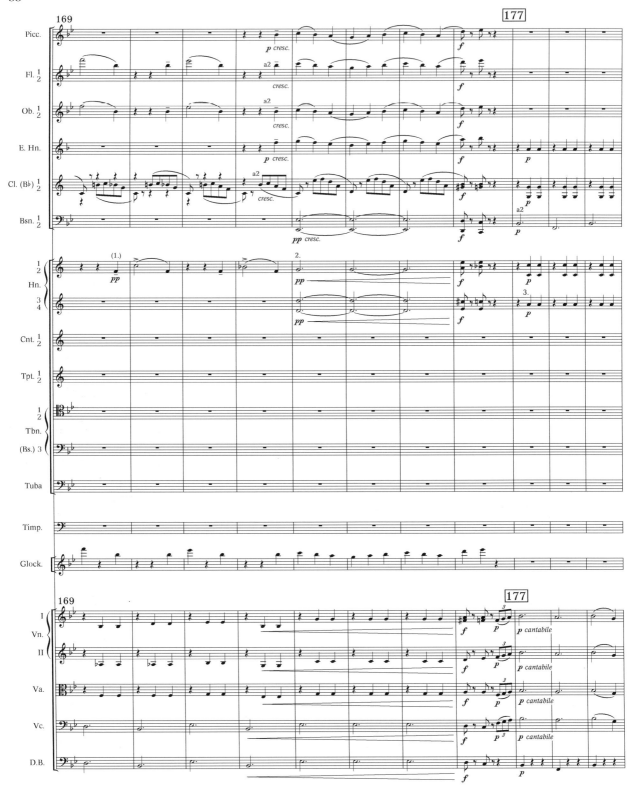

40437

94

40437